"MORNING VICAR"

HUMOROUS MONOLOGUES

by

ALISON HUNT

MOORLEY'S Print & Publishing

ISBN 0 86071 394 6

MOORLEY'S Print & Publishing

23 Park Rd., Ilkeston, Derbys DE7 5DA
Tel/Fax: (0115) 932 0643

EXTRA HELP IN THE VESTRY

Morning Vicar! I'm 'Extra help in the vestry'. You know.....you advertised in the magazine?

Well here I am.....save you the trouble of an interview I thought I'd just turn up as I'm not on tea and coffee this week.

Now.....I've rearranged the cassocks in the wardrobe here, big ones on the right and getting smaller down to the little ones on the left. Yes, I know they were arranged the other way over but then I'm left-handed so it'll be easier this way.

I've done that little bit of washing up on the draining board only I wasn't sure how to put away, so I just put the goblets in the cupboard with the mugs and things and the little silver plates in the other cupboard with the crockery that comes out when the bishop's here. I'll soon learn.

I was shocked by the state of your surplice, Vicar. Funny how you don't see from the congregation but up close it's all stains. What've you been doing? Drying your hands on it? I've got it in soak. You'll have to wear this one, I got it from the head chorister, his mother's a lovely woman, she keeps him spotless. I had a bit of a tussle dragging it out of the boy's hands, but I soon fixed the rip and it won't show being as it's at the back. Good job you're only little, eh?

No.....I beg pardon Vicar but the photocopier is jammed this morning. They'll have to share the hymn sheet one between three when the time comes. Don't worry, they're used to it. I wanted to put through a copy of our tea rota, but it didn't come out too well, so I did what the verger does. I took the front off it and ran my handkerchief through between the rollers. Funny, I've seen his hankie go through dozens of times but mine seems to have got eaten. Don't you worry Vicar I've got plenty more. I'm not going to sue you over the cost of a hankie, that's not what friends are for now is it?

Is this your sermon Vicar? I had a quick squint and I hope you don't mind my saying so, but they won't want to hear about money again this week. Not after that begging sermon you did last week. I don't mind telling you there were some bad comments come back at me over the tea urn later.

There are those in this parish who would sooner not be asked to give anything to the organist when he leaves either. He's too big for his boots, that one. All those twiddly bits between the verses so that a body doesn't know when to start singing. Bill Crane nearly swallowed his false teeth with laughing when you were left high and dry during verse four. 'Bore it up triumphant', you were singing all alone into your microphone and Sid Bray gives you a round of applause.

And there's another thing.....Sid and I were next to each other at the altar rail last week, well you must have noticed it, he takes that dirty drooping moustache for a swim in the chalice each week, made me shudder to think how close I'd come to kneeling the far side of him. Instead of which there was your own lady wife demurely receiving without giving Sid's facial hair a second thought. She's a wonderful woman.

Is this how you work the monitor then? Look there's old Mrs. Clerke. Looks like she's talking to Maudie again. They had a most terrible dust up Vicar after all those things you said to Maudie about how her flower arranging was really coming along a treat.

Oh I know you meant no harm by it but the big showy arrangement that everyone moaned about was Mrs. Clerke's effort you see and you didn't really ought to have assumed it was dying just because it was sort of hanging limp like. I understand it was fresh that day. An easy mistake to make Vicar, lots of people made it, but it was just that Mrs. Clerke heard you tell Maudie to throw it out and try her hand because she couldn't do worse. The pair of them have been at daggers drawn all week.

Whoops! There goes Mrs. O'Brian, my she did take a tumble. It's that son of hers. Went away to theological college and came back genuflecting, she never does seem to expect it of him and there she went right over his head.

Oh look there's that little grandson of yours Vicar. Where's your daughter? Young Philip is swinging all along the brass altar rail.

I'll go out and polish it, shall I? No? Well there'll be comments after about his little sticky dabs all over it, it's up to you Vicar.....

Bishop!..... Well this is a surprise. What's that all down your front? You just step over here and I'll sponge you down. There we are..... No there's no time for a towel now, the choir have seen you and they're already leaving their vestry. Never mind you'll just have to drip dry. Off you all go and don't worry about a thing, I'll be waiting here to receive you when you get back and I can watch the whole thing on this little telly.

THE AUTUMN FAIR

Morning Vicar! I didn't want to phone as I know it's your day off and you shouldn't really be disturbed. I thought if I called good and early it wouldn't cut into your day so much.

You shouldn't stand here in your pyjamas, you'll catch your death, let's go indoors shall we? That's better.

Well now Vicar I've got to tell you that there are a few problems with the Autumn fair this year. I knew you would want to know straight away that Doreen and Mrs. Milner are arguing about the jam.

It seems that somebody told Doreen that she was responsible for the Marmalade and as you know Mrs. Milner always makes that. So the Jam stall is in chaos.

The Blood donors had an accident in the hall last week and there's the remains of about two pints of 'O' positive all up the wall by the gents.

You alright Vicar? My you look pale! Anyway, I've had young Toby in there all yesterday trying to get the stuff off the wall, freshly decorated we were too Vicar, as you know, all that white spoiled.

The Sunday School promised to make a chart of Noah's flood to cover the worst of the damage, but that makes another problem because it's right where Flo always has the tombola and she says the public won't see her poster if there's a colourful picture of Noah on the wall just where she does her advertising. So she's up in arms.

I've offered her the warmer placement over near the kitchen but unfortunately, she went and said that the smell of the annual shepherds pie bake for the punters' lunches would make her feel sick. I say unfortunate because she was overheard by the girl guides and they are planning strike action in the kitchen now.

Have you got any spare sheets? No I don't suppose you have, nor has anyone else, Vicar, I was hoping to placate the guides with a few. You see they're organising the entertainment in the afternoon and they need sheets to do the scenery or something.

You certainly put your foot in it there, didn't you Vicar, laugh.....I nearly wept with it. Running up the steps to the stage like that to try and free Mrs. Mint from the ropes..... The Brownies doing their knotting practice. Now I'll let you into a secret there Vicar, the little imps have left the window cords in a dreadful mess, it's doubtful whether we shall ever manage to lower the blinds again.

Still it should be dark outside by the time you want to show those slides of the Holy Land and probably there won't be that many people interested. Anyway there'll be a lot less in the hall paying to see them when word gets out that they can see them just as well from outside in the car park and still be able to talk and drink their beer at the same time.

Now don't you worry about the face painting, I've got my little niece onto it. You know we were stuck because Hazel wouldn't do it this year? My Joanne has been dying to have a go and she's been practising on her little brother. Yesterday he looked all pink from having had the stuff scrubbed out of his hairline.

Joanne reckons that if she raffles your face Vicar we could raise quite a bit. You know, we make an announcement that if there's enough money raised you'll have your face done, and then you have to make a great show of not wanting it painted, that way we make more money. She reckons a clown and then we dare you to take evensong with the paint still on, place bets, well that's not strictly spiritual so we'll do a sort of sponsorship thing. I've told her what a good sport you are so that's alright, isn't it Vicar? I didn't think you'd object.

Can I get you a coffee or anything, you're looking a little pale Vicar? Let's draw the curtains in here, it's going to be a really fine day for your holiday, Vicar. Are you going anywhere nice?   I only ask because I know you sometimes drive down to the cottage with your good lady, and my Gladys and I thought we might drop in on you for a light luncheon later on. I would stop and take breakfast with you both but I notice that your good lady is still in bed and I wouldn't like to intrude, so I'll bid you good day Vicar.

Don't forget to look out for us at lunchtime, will you?

HOSPITAL VISITING

Morning Vicar! Surprised to see me? I've not done hospital visiting before but I must say I've had a lovely time so far. I've been preparing the ground for you, Vicar.

Mind you I thought you were going to miss Kathy Phipps altogether, poor old dear. I had to hold her nose to see if she'd open her mouth to breathe. Disappointing really as I've never seen the administering of the last rites.

Now I know you hate the sight of blood so I'd advise against seeing Mr. Briscoe. He's got a couple of pints on a drip, and the young nurse made a bit of a mess of his hand with the needle. I've put his hand under the coverlet for you and I hung Mr. Briscoe's dressing gown over the drip stand.

Then unfortunately, Mrs. Carlisle in the next bed half woke up and thought she saw her husband. She started talking to the dressing gown, so I opened it up to show her what was underneath and she screamed and fainted away!

Sister suggested I should come down this end of the ward and you know I'm rather glad I did. Daisy Grimes is down here, Vicar, did you know that? Says she wants a Eucharist but I don't know quite what to suggest Vicar. I'm not sure how you'll manage it because she has got a sign saying, 'Nil by mouth'. I suppose you could get someone to inject the blessed sacrament into a vein with a needle and put the wafer on 'hold'.

I'm so glad you took the trouble to get dressed up Vicar because it really helps the heathen elements to respect you properly, especially with you being so short and all. I've got that little table out for you and when I told Sister about your little difficulty in the height department she very kindly agreed to let you stand on that little set of steps so that everybody can see you.

There's not very many that can manage to sing hymns just at present, but I make it four counting you and me, I don't mind staying if you like.

Oh! Don't mind him, Vicar. That's just Fred Binney, we're good friends now, it's just his way. He's such a tease, he's been begging me to go away ever since I got here, just his little joke, we have an understanding and I know he doesn't mean it. Isn't that right Fred?.....

I'm terribly sorry you had to hear that, Vicar, just remember we're not all chosen, but we are all loved and to err is human but to forgive, divine.....

Oh.....well you are taking it well, is there any need to laugh quite so violently, Vicar? That's better, you must think of your image.

You'll love Miss Entwhistle's gall stones. I've never seen so many. She's going to make jewellery, you know, earrings and such like. My idea. I thought it would liven up the next W.I. meeting. Be a novelty on the craft stall later, and God knows they need all the help they can get. It'd be a bit like selling Holy Relics, wouldn't it, Vicar?

I don't know how come so much of the parish is in this place at the moment. Young Matthew Harris is downstairs having his stomach pumped out. I saw him as I came in, don't know what it was he'd eaten, I crept in to his little cubicle where he was lying all alone and green looking, poor little mite. I didn't stop long, just slipped him a Mars bar and crept away. You have to know how to handle kids.

I'm thinking of talking to someone about becoming a hospital porter you know..... Goodness, that's Fred making that terrible noise! It looks like he's trying to get out of bed. You'd better go and stop him putting that crushed foot on the floor, Vicar, while I go and find Sister. I wonder what the poor man can be thinking of!.....

Oh, by the way, in case I forget, they have lunch early here, so I thought, if you time it right, you can probably fit the prayers in while they eat their first course and then slip the Eucharist in before pudding, nice and tidy, and then you'll be away in time for that funeral at two.

ECUMENICAL SERVICE

Morning Vicar! I've been following you all the way from the station. Did you know we were on the same train? I felt sure that you had seen me, but no. My word you can move quickly for such a little man. If I didn't know better I'd say you were deliberately trying to run away from me.

Silly really.....as I'm sure you are anxious to discuss Sunday's service with me. You know I'm being a sidesman for the big ecumenical 'do'? I've not been a sidesman before but I assume it'll be easy to see who's who?

Do you think we should introduce a little dish of Holy Water for the Catholics to make them feel at home? Or is there a feeling that it could lead some of our own flock to start taking up Roman ways? Anyway, I guess the Catholics will be easy to spot because they'll be looking around for something to kiss or cross themselves in front of. I thought I'd put the Catholics all together at the front where you can keep your eye on them.

As for the regulars, well, we'd mostly be comfortable at the back in the dark, that's how we Anglicans like to be. I just wondered where you'd like the 'Happy Clappy' lot, and don't say 'outside in the car park' Vicar, we must be hospitable! I had thought to put them in the middle, but then there's bits of the service that the regulars won't see on account of the forest of waving arms.

By the way, will there be anything to actively **encourage** that kind of thing? I mean, if you plan modern chorus type hymns, I'll put the word out. Not that we mind but it's just that there are those who'll want the chance not to come.....and others much more liberal minded, Vicar, who'll just like warnings about how embarrassing it's all likely to get.

The wife wondered if we should put a few Icons about to make the orthodox people feel more at home. Oh, you don't think we'll get any..... Don't they like the happy clappy idea either?

Well, now that's a shame, 'cause you know what I've always said about our church? It's so unthreatening and private that you could lie down and die on a back pew one Sunday and not be altogether certain of being found until the Sunday morning after, and that only if somebody happened to look. Personally I like it that way.

What about the Baptists and the Methodists? Do they know about the Eucharist? I mean will they know what to do? How will you know Vicar which ones qualify? Should I conduct a little survey as the people come into church, you know, ask them to put their hands up if they've had a good honest Confirmation?

Maybe I'll just get Doris to make a couple of discreet notices to put across the main aisle on a banner. Something like 'Do not attempt to take the blessed sacrament if you know in your heart that you don't qualify!' That takes the responsibility off your little shoulders, doesn't it Vicar?

Don't you worry we're all right behind you. I daresay there'll be folk there who'll want a pretty emotional kind of a 'do' but you just stick to your guns. After all they aren't your regulars, they'll be gone again as soon as you've finished with them. It's your job to just get up there and show them all how it should be done. Don't you be afraid of any of them.

I hope you won't go watering the wine down or putting Ribena out for the Methodists. If there's any of that you'll have to have two different distribution points. Shall I get Doris to knock up a couple of extra signs while she's about it? 'Fruit of the vine' say, on one and 'Non-Biblical beverage' on the other.

What do you think?

———————————————

NO GOSSIP PLEASE,
WE'RE CHRISTIANS!

Morning Vicar! Thought I'd find you here. I heard a whisper that you sometimes come to the Lady Chapel at about this time on a Tuesday to be quiet like.

It's about those whispers that I wanted to talk. Shall we get up off our knees, Vicar, I find the tiles really hard? More comfy to be sitting, eh?

Well now, one of those little whispers came back to my Gladys over coffee in the vestry. That Mrs. Pargeter really upset her I can tell you.

Now we're not given to gossip as you know Vicar, but it seems that the word has got out that you don't really like the help that me and my Gladys give you..... there! I knew you'd be shocked to hear it!

I told my Gladys that Mrs. Pargeter's no better than she should be. It was her that caused all that trouble with the Nativity play. Made little Bill Wilkins cry on stage.

Well it seems that Mrs. Pargeter's best nightie had been borrowed without her knowledge, to use for Angel Gabriel. Young Bill appears wearing it minutes before the show and Mrs. Pargeter does her pieces and upsets him.

Mind you he got his own back, remember Vicar? Just as he's announcing the Good News to Mary, he wets himself. Mrs. Pargeter's face was a picture. That's how the rumour started about her being pregnant Vicar, you heard that one?

Well it all started with the Nativity play, Bill's accident made Mrs. Pargeter look so pale that Joyce, well you know there's never been any love lost between Joyce and her, or Joyce and anyone else for that matter. Anyway, Joyce muttered something from the pew in front and the stories all began.

Really silly because you know there's been all that trouble in Mrs. Pargeter's life Vicar? I mean she and her husband haven't slept in the same room for years now. So if it's true then who's baby is it, I'd like to know? You wait till I tell my Gladys! I told her that Mrs. Pargeter was no better than she should be. That proves it!

No Vicar, don't hold up your hands that way.....I'll say it for you, you know any information is safe with me. I don't hold with gossip.

Gladys and I are real Christians, we wouldn't dream of saying a word to a soul. That goes for your other little secret, you know. Now that came to us by a really odd route.

I was clipping my hedge and old man Riley was clipping the far side of the same hedge and his young nephew comes bounding over and says, 'You know the Vicar's going in hospital next month? I'm going to have words with the verger' he says, 'I reckon while the man's laid up we'll get the naive altar shifted round and the seats put in a friendly semi-circle. He's an old fogey'..... sorry Vicar, just repeating what I heard, 'He's an old fogey and he'll like it when he gets back and finds the parish is used to it that way.'

Of course I didn't pop up and ask the question, but Mr. Riley asked it for me. I knew you were having pains Vicar, but I didn't know you'd been for a Barium Meal. If I'd known Gladys and I could have run you to the hospital, she has her corns seen to regular and we're often going that way. Now why didn't you say?

Seems you did really well. Young Janet More is a nurse there, bless her, and she's furnished people with the truth. Well it stops rumours if someone's clear about their facts doesn't it? So Vicar, if it isn't an ulcer what is it? Stress I expect.

You should take a holiday after your little exploratory, Vicar. Don't you worry about a thing, we'll handle everything while you're away. I know you think you're indispensable, but nobody is that, you know. I'm dying to try my hand at a sermon.....

So that's settled then, I'll tell the church wardens that you're to have at least six months off. If I hurry I'll just catch Andrew this morning. He's due at the dentist in ten minutes.

Must rush, no don't delay me or I'll miss him, he'll be in no fit state to speak to me afterwards, I believe he's having a couple of extractions. He'll be happier talking to me first. I expect he'll be glad I showed up to take his mind off things.

MOORLEY'S

are growing Publishers, adding several new titles to our list each year. We also undertake private publications and commissioned works.

Our range of publications includes: **Books of Verse**
Devotional Poetry
Recitations
Drama
Bible Plays
Sketches
Nativity Plays
Passiontide Plays
Easter Plays
Demonstrations
Resource Books
Assembly Material
Songs & Musicals
Children's Addresses
Prayers & Graces
Daily Readings
Books for Speakers
Activity Books
Quizzes
Puzzles
Painting Books
Daily Readings
Church Stationery
Notice Books
Cradle Rolls
Hymn Board Numbers

Please send a S.A.E. (approx 9" x 6") for the current catalogue or consult your local Christian Bookshop who should stock or be able to order our titles.